INSPIRE

HAIR FASHION FOR SALON CLIENTS

Dressing Up

Brides, Up Dos, Formals

VOLUME 40

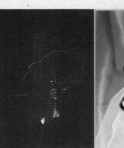

Contents

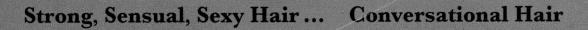

Strong, Sensual, Sexy Hair... Conversational Hair

The word on the street is **strong, sensual, sexy hair!**
Hair that's discussed... Hair that's talked about.

It's **hip hop** and oh so cool...

The runway models wear it,
everyone else wants it!   What is it?

Shredded Hair...
Reversible Hair!

Artec

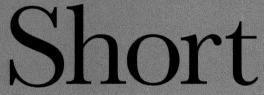

ARTEC

YOSH FOR HAIR
HAIR: YOSH TOYA
PHOTO: BARRY YEE

I emphasized the *versatility* of a classic hairstyle.

Demonstrating that a hairstyle can maintain it's *classic elegance* with a refreshing trendy touch.

Highlighting the *movement* of the hairstyle I created a free flowing look.

Yosh Toya

SALON FRANCESCO
HAIR: LEWIS MOORE
MAKE-UP: LOUISE JAMES
PHOTO: PETER DELLICOMPAGNI

The Flipside Collection - Inspiration

Polished and refined in contrast with sultry and temperamental attitude.

Contrast − Black & White − Changeable − Split Personalities − Texture − Smooth − Strong

BEFORE

CHRIS & SONYA DOVE

YELLOW STRAWBERRY
HAIR: TODD FINNEY
MAKE-UP: DORIS FINNEY
PHOTO: TOM CARSON

YELLOW STRAWBERRY
HAIR: GEORGE PANAGIOTOPOULOS
MAKE-UP: AUGUST WERNER
PHOTO: TOM CARSON

YELLOW STRAWBERRY
HAIR: DEBBY RUSSEK
MAKE-UP: KRIS MCDONALD
PHOTO: TOM CARSON

YELLOW STRAWBERRY
HAIR: RICHARD WEINTRAUB
PHOTO: TOM CARSON

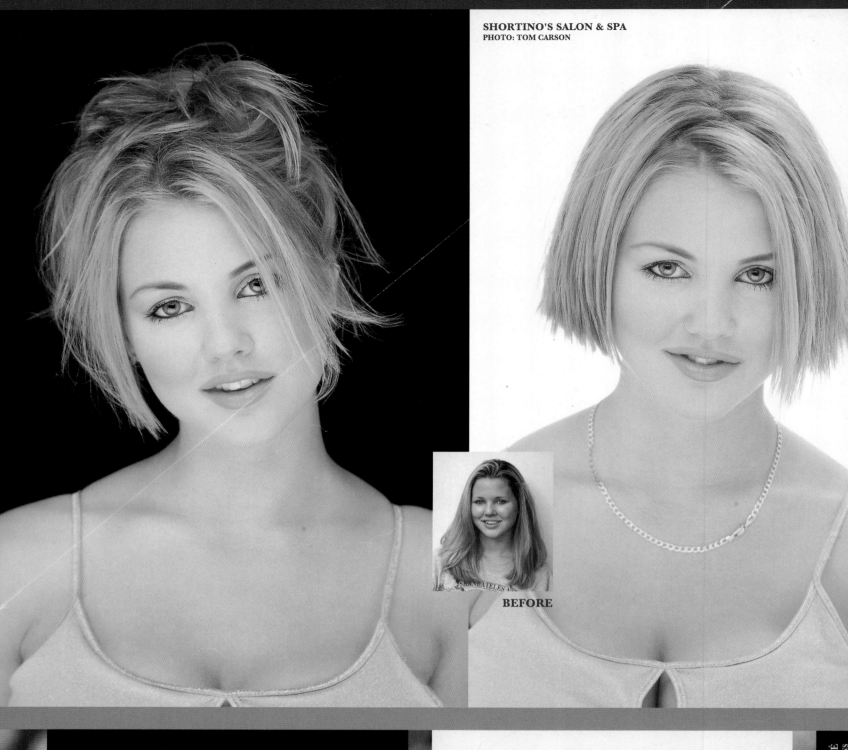

SHORTINO'S SALON & SPA
PHOTO: TOM CARSON

BEFORE

BEFORE

SHORTINO'S SALON & SPA
PHOTO: TOM CARSON

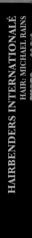

HAIRBENDERS INTERNATIONALÉ
HAIR: MICHAEL RAINS

SHORTINO'S SALON & SPA
PHOTO: TOM CARSON

SHORTINO'S SALON & SPA
PHOTO: TOM CARSON

BEFORE

HAIRBENDERS INTERNATIONALÉ
HAIR: ELIZABETH KINCAID
PHOTO: TOM CARSON

HAIRBENDERS INTERNATIONALÉ
HAIR: BOBBY FAIRBANKS
PHOTO: TOM CARSON

HUGO SA
HAIR: COURTNEY ASHW
PHOTO:

Inspired by
fashion and
the direction
of clothing.

Strong images
with soft texture,
definite shapes
and shine.

Francesco Group

SALON FRANCESCO
HAIR: SIMON PARSONS
MAKE-UP: LOUISE PARSONS
PHOTO: PETER DELLICOMPAGNI

ECLIPS SALON & DAY SPA
HAIR: ERIC HELTON
PHOTO: DEBBIE PRIZZIA

HUGO SALON
HAIR: TONI KIM
PHOTO: HUGO

13

PON INTERNATIONAL
HAIR: TODD & AMBER SNOW
MAKE-UP: JAIME QUEENIN
PHOTO: TAGGART-WINTERHALTER

For a shorter look the bob is **razor cut** with **internal texture** to help dictate the overall shape.

The **medium copper base** is accented with **dark absorbent lowlights** and **bright reflective highlights**.

Todd and Amber Snow - Pon International

PON INTERNATIONAL
HAIR & MAKE-UP: TAMMY KAHLEN
PHOTO: TAGGART-WINTERHALTER

PARAGON
HAIR: AARON BAKER
MAKE-UP: JAIME QUEENIN
PHOTO: TAGGART-WINTERHALTER

By using a razor the basic bob is **shattered at the edges** – shard like pieces are added for texture. The two-tone warm auburn color is boldly accented by a darker red brown hue for **ravenous depth.**

Pon Seradeth - Pon International

IMAGES SALON
HAIR: RON PEREZ/LINDA RAMOS
MAKE-UP: JAIME QUEENIN
PHOTO: TAGGART-WINTERHALTER

A youthful and wildly modern style with **untamed color** comes all wrapped in one fabulous head of hair.

Ron Perez & Linda Ramos
Images Salon

PON INTERNATIONAL
HAIR: PON SARADETH
MAKE-UP: JAIME QUEENIN
PHOTO: TAGGART-WINTERHALTER

15

Freehand texture on an ultra short base, this *platinum bombshell* has a rich honey tone cast. A spunky fun style that's easy to care for and style.

Laura Orozco & Kristin Atkinson
Empire Salon

EMPIRE SALON
HAIR: LAURA OROZCO / KRISTIN ATKINSON
MAKE-UP: JAIME QUEENIN
PHOTO: TAGGART-WINTERHALTER

IMAGES SALON
HAIR: RITA BAGLIETTO-MILES / LINDA RAMOS
MAKE-UP: JAIME QUEENIN
PHOTO: TAGGART-WINTERHALTER

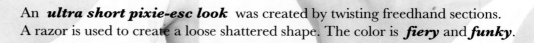

An *ultra short pixie-esc look* was created by twisting freehand sections. A razor is used to create a loose shattered shape. The color is *fiery* and *funky*.

Rita Baglietto Miles & Linda Ramos - Images Salon

16

TRIBE SALON
HAIR: PAMELA PERETTIE
MAKE-UP: JAIME QUEENIN
PHOTO: TAGGART-WINTERHALTER

FORTELESCE THE SALON
HAIR: MARGIT AARON / JENELLE SMITH
MAKE-UP: JAMIE QUEENIN
PHOTO: TAGGART-WINTERHALTER

SALON AND SPA GREGORIES
HAIR: TEAM GREGORIES
MAKE-UP: KARIN NOEL FOR PRISS
PHOTO: TAGGART-WINTERHALTER

SALON AND SPA GREGORIES
HAIR: TEAM GREGORIES
MAKE-UP: KARIN NOEL FOR PRISS
PHOTO: TAGGART-WINTERHALTER

HAIRBENDERS INTERNATIONALÉ
HAIR: ELIZABETH KINCAID
PHOTO: TOM CARSON

HAIRBENDERS INTERNATIONALÉ
HAIR: ELIZABETH KINCAID
PHOTO: TOM CARSON

HAIRBENDERS INTERNATIONALÉ
HAIR: ELIZABETH KINCAID
PHOTO: TOM CARSON

HAIRBENDERS INTERNATIONALÉ
HAIR: LILY VISHENCHUK
PHOTO: TOM CARSON

HAIRBENDERS INTERNATIONALÉ
HAIR: MICHAEL RAINS
PHOTO: TOM CARSON

Medium

HAIRBENDERS INTERNATIONALÉ
HAIR: ELIZABETH KINCAID
PHOTO: TOM CARSON

HAIRBENDERS INTERNATIONALÉ
HAIR: AMY SOUTHERLAND
PHOTO: TOM CARSON

BEFORE

Fresh warm looks for the upcoming season.   Umbertos

UMBERTO'S
HAIR: UMBERTO/NINA
MAKE-UP: DALYNN
PHOTO: UMBERTO

RENAISSANCE SALON
HAIR: KATIE MURPHY
MAKE-UP: CATHERINE RAFFAELE
PHOTO: ERIC VON LOCKHART

ECLIPS SALON & DAY SPA
HAIR & MAKE-UP: DEBBIE PRIZZIA

UMBERTO'S
HAIR: UMBERTO/NINA
PHOTO: UMBERTO

HAIRBOUTIQUE.COM
HAIR: BARBARA LHOTAN
MAKE-UP: CATHERINE RAFFAELE
PHOTO: ERIC VON LOCKHART

25

**DEFRANCO SPAGNOLO
SALON / DAYSPA**
HAIR: RENE SPAGNOLO / LORI TEGANO
MAKE-UP: CARRIE SPAGNOLO
PHOTO: RICHARD GARDNER

Unleashed!

Step away from convention with styles that unleash pure potential.

Unleashed focuses on the contrast between short and long, while marrying the two into wearable modern shapes. In each of the looks, sliced overlapping brings the structure together.

Anthony Cristiano
Mario Tricoci Hair
Salons & Day Spas

EMPIRE SALON
HAIR: ANNIE BENLO
MAKE-UP: JULIE STODDARD
PHOTO: TAGGART-WINTERHALTER

DEFRANCO SPAGNOLO
SALON / DAYSPA
HAIR: RENE SPAGNOLO / NICOLE KLETT
MAKE-UP: CARRIE SPAGNOLO
PHOTO: RICHARD GARDNER

EMPIRE SALON
HAIR: LAURA OROZCO
MAKE-UP: JULIE STODDARD
PHOTO: TAGGART-WINTERHALTER

Color is strong and bold. Shapes express strong
graphic outlines, introducing an asymmetrical silhouette.
The Look is lived in – not the appearance of over styled,
over worked hair.

Robert Bushy - Salon 2000

SALON 2000
HAIR: ROBERT J. BUSHY
MAKE-UP: MICHE NELSON
PHOTO: TOM MCINVAILLE

SALON JKL
HAIR: JAMIE KOGER - LAPRAIRIE
MAKE-UP: GLENN MOSLEY
PHOTO: TAGGART-WINTERHALTER

FANTASTIC SAMS
HAIR: BETH ORZECHOWSKI
PHOTO: TAGGART-WINTERHALTER

BEFORE

PETER THOMAS HAIR DESIGN
HAIR: KELSEA OSBORNE
MAKE-UP: KELSEA OSBORNE
PHOTO: DEBORAH SIMONS

YELLOW STRAWBERRY
HAIR: RICHARD WEINTRAUB
MAKE-UP: MICHELLE
PHOTO: TOM CARSON

SALON FRANCESCO
HAIR: SIMON PARSONS
MAKE-UP: LOUISE PURVES
PHOTO: PETER DELLICOMPAGNI

SHORTINO'S SALON & SPA
HAIR: STEPHANIE

JENNY HEROUX
MAKE-UP: JAMIE QUEENIN
PHOTO: TAGGART-WINTERHALTER

BEFORE

ELIZABETH BENKE & ASSOCIATES
SALON & COLOR STUDIO
PHOTO: JAMIE HANKIN

DIZIN SALON
HAIR: BETH ECKEL
PHOTO: BETH ECKEL

LONG

Mid Range Madness

This mid length razor cut was done inside out for the ultimate in texture. The color is a rich copper gold with golden blonde highlights to define the cut.

Steve Hernandez
Vogue Salon

Long layers were achieved by extreme slicing for outside texture. For the color - a true natural beige was created over a deep chocolate and caramel blocks of color.

Team Gregories - Salon and Spa Gregories

SALON AND SPA GREGORIES
HAIR: TEAM GREGORIES
MAKE-UP: KARIN NOEL FOR PRISS
PHOTO: TAGGART-WINTERHALTER

A forward graduation cut is a face-framing look that can be achieved by styling with mousse before blow-drying with a large round brush.

Team Gregories - Salon and Spa Gregories

SCULPT SALON
HAIR: GEORGE ALDARETE/HUGO URIAS
MAKE-UP: JOE MATKE
PHOTO: TAGGART-WINTERHALTER

LONG

BEFORE

35

MARIO TRICOCI HAIR SALONS & DAY SPAS
HAIR: MARIO TRICOCI ARTISTIC TEAM
MAKE-UP: COSE COSMETICS
PHOTO: AKIN GIRAV

ARTEC

HUGO SALON
HAIR: JESSICA WILSON
PHOTO: HUGO

HUGO SALON
HAIR: JESSICA WILSON
PHOTO: HUGO

HUGO SALON
HAIR: TONI KIM
PHOTO: HUGO

MARIO TRICOCI HAIR SALONS & DAY SPAS
HAIR: MARIO TRICOCI ARTISTIC TEAM
MAKE-UP: COSE COSMETICS
PHOTO: AKIN GIRAV

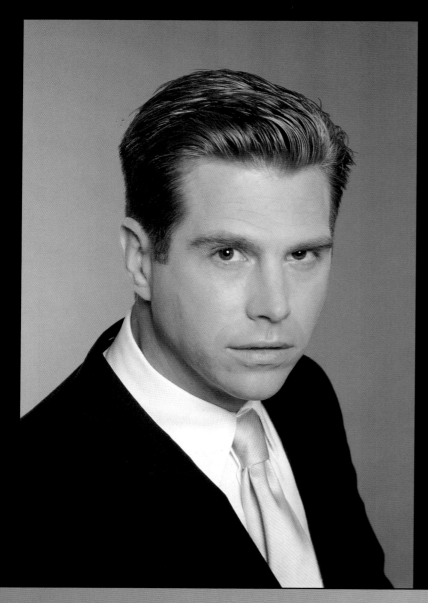

A perfect length for business. This short cut has clipper cut sides and a blended but slightly longer top. A very easy style to upkeep.

Yong Kim - Fantastic Sam's

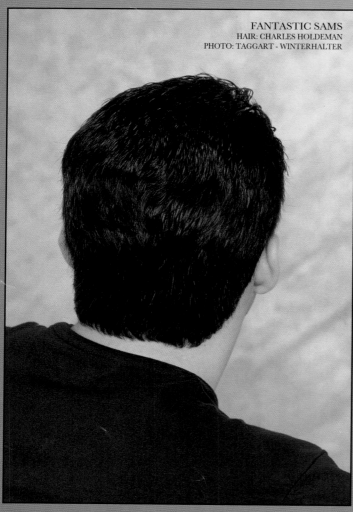

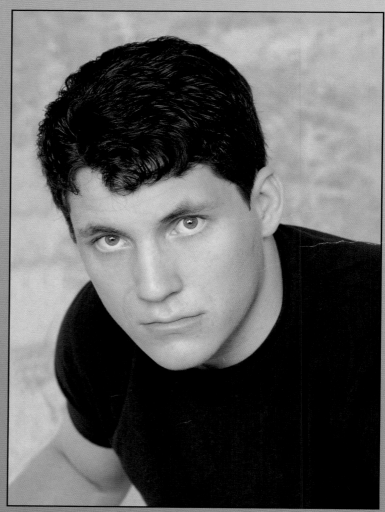

A short men's taper cut that has a slightly longer top and front section that is left curly for texture.

Charles Holdeman - Fantastic Sam's

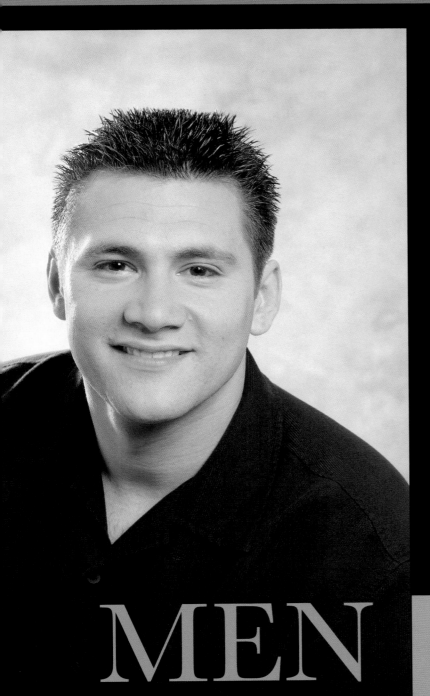

An ultra short clipper cut crop is lightly spiked by using a gel product in the hair.

Jennifer Metzger - Fantastic Sam's

MEN

An ultra short clippered fade that sports a bit of length on top. A versatile yet cool cut that has many styling options. Perfect with curl or wave.

Sandy Nguyen - Fantastic Sam's

LONG

39

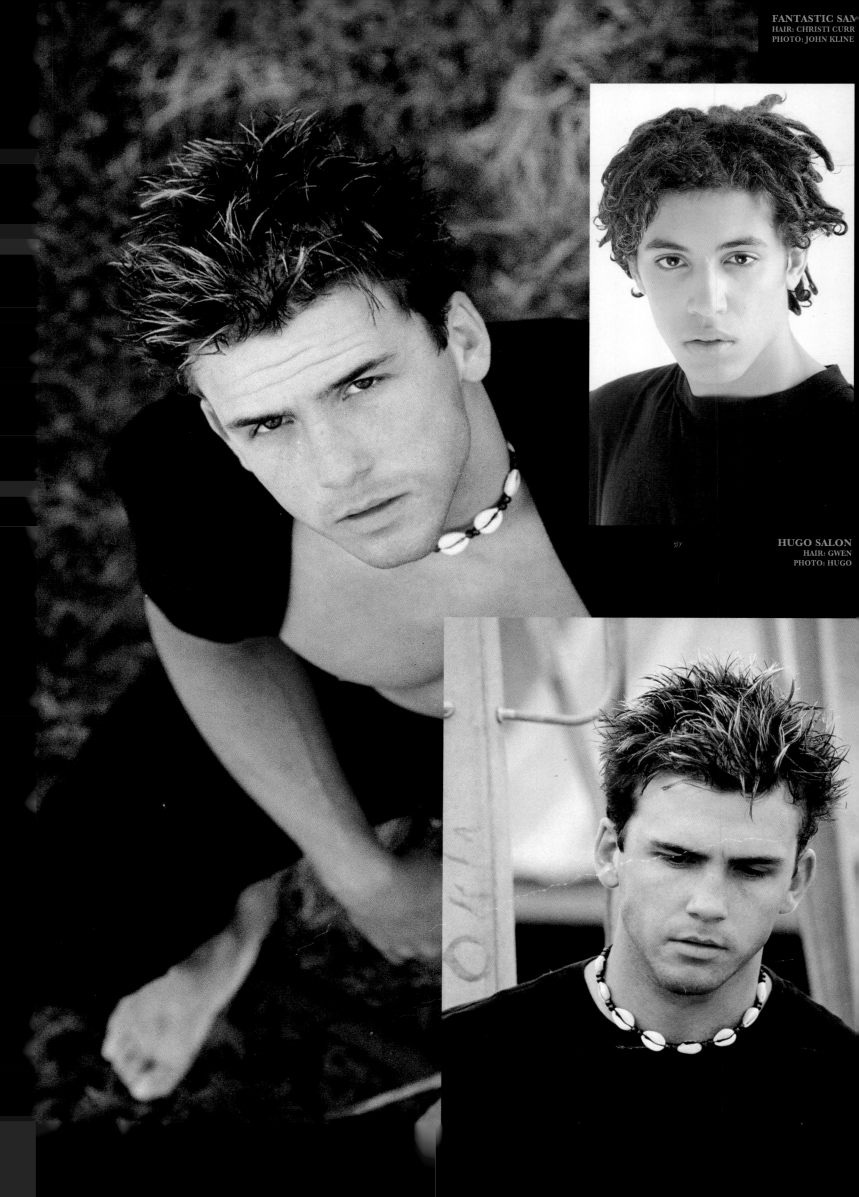

FANTASTIC SAM
HAIR: CHRISTI CURR
PHOTO: JOHN KLINE

HUGO SALON
HAIR: GWEN
PHOTO: HUGO

SCULPT SALON
HAIR: GEORGE ALDERETE / HUGO URIAS
MAKE-UP: JOE MATKE
PHOTO: TAGGART - WINTERHALTER

BEFORE

EMPIRE SALON
HAIR: KIMMI LE
MAKE-UP: JULIE STODDARD
PHOTO: TAGGART- WINTERHALTER

PLANET SALON
HAIR: NIC PAUL
PHOTO: CHRIS REED

PLANET SALON
HAIR: MARCY COMBS
PHOTO: CHRIS REED

PLANET SALON
HAIR: THOMAS DYSARZ
PHOTO: CHRIS REED

PLANET SALON
HAIR: DONNA SPARKS
PHOTO: CHRIS REED

PLANET SALON
HAIR: SARA MADISON
PHOTO: CHRIS REED

LONG

MLD III SALON
HAIR: BILL BAKER
PHOTO: BILL BAKER

MLD III SALON
HAIR: SANDRA CHANDLER
PHOTO: BILL BAKER

L'IMAGE SALONS
HAIR: MONIKA NORMAN
PHOTO: DAYTON MAST

DIZIN SALON
HAIR: BETH ECKEL
PHOTO: BETH ECKEL

You Lookin' At Me?

This edgy look will command Respect.

This short haircut is razored out for exaggerated texture with accent highlights placed mainly in the front hairline to create movement and dimension.

Monika Norman
L'Image Salons

TOUGH ENOUGH

Hair is cut short
and the perimeter
outlined with shears
for over-the-top texture.
Blue sheer gloss is applied
for a punch of shine.

Monika Norman
L'Image Salons

TOO COOL

There is nothing subtle about this bad boy look.
Extreme texture is achieved through a razor cut
that allows hair to be molded into a super-cool do.

Eduardo Cantu - L'image Salons

LONG

UMBERTO'S

45

SPECIAL Collections

BEFORE

BARBARA LHOTAN
MAKE-UP: CATHERINE RAFFAELE
PHOTO: ERIC VON LOCKHART

BEFORE

CARLA D'AMICO FORD
MAKE-UP: CATHERINE RAFFAELE
PHOTO: ERIC VON LOCKHART

BEFORE

TOM HARRIS
MAKE-UP: CATHERINE RAFFAELE
PHOTO: ERIC VON LOCKHART

BARBARA LHOTAN
MAKE-UP: CATHERINE RAFFAELE
PHOTO: ERIC VON LOCKHART

SPECIAL Collections

BEFORE

48

BEFORE

PON INTERNATIONAL
HAIR: JENNIFER HAYS
MAKE-UP: JAMIE QUEENIN
PHOTO: TAGGART - WINTERHALTER

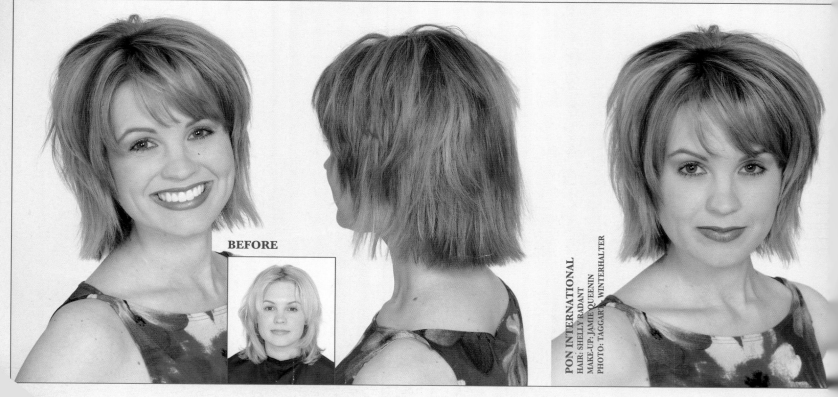

BEFORE

PON INTERNATIONAL
HAIR: SHELLY RADANT
MAKE-UP: JAMIE QUEENIN
PHOTO: TAGGART - WINTERHALTER

BEFORE

BEFORE

PON INTERNATIONAL
HAIR: PON SARADETH
MAKE-UP: JAMIE QUEENIN
PHOTO: TAGGART - WINTERHALTER

SPECIAL Collections

YELLOW STRAWBERRY GLOBAL SALONS
HAIR: GINA VITALE
MAKE-UP: GINA VITALE
PHOTO: TOM CARSON

KAREN O"DONNELL NESBIT
PHOTO: LEE GODBURN

50

Formals

FORMALS

SHORTINO'S SALON & SPA

DEFRANCO SPAGNOLO SALON / DAYSPA
HAIR: RENE SPAGNOLO / AMANI YASSIME
MAKE-UP: CARRIE SPAGNOLO

51

FORTELESCE THE SALON
HAIR: MARGIT AARON
MAKE-UP: JAMIE QUEENIN
PHOTO: TAGGART - WINTERHATLER

TROY FOUSTINO SALONS
HAIR: TROY FOUSTINO/PAULETTE FURTADO
MAKE-UP: ROSE MARIE
PHOTO: TAGGART - WINTERHATLER

PETER BOKANOSKI
MAKE-UP: ROSE MARIE
PHOTO: TAGGART - WINTERHATLER

TRIBE SALON
HAIR: PAMELA PERETTIE
MAKE-UP: JAMIE QUEENIN
PHOTO: TAGGART - WINTERHATLER

SASKIA SEVEY
MAKE-UP: ROSE MARIE
PHOTO: TAGGART - WINTERHATLER

TRIBE SALON
MAKE-UP: JAMIE QUEENIN

TRIBE SALON
HAIR: THU NGUUYEN
MAKE-UP: JAMIE QUEENIN
PHOTO: TAGGART - WINTERHATLER

FORMALS

53

RENAISSANCE SALON
HAIR: BARBARA LHOTAN / KATIE MURPHY
MAKE-UP: CATHERINE RAFFAELE
PHOTO: ERIC VON LOCKHART

RENAISSANCE SALON
HAIR: BARBARA LHOTAN / KATIE MURPHY
MAKE-UP: CATHERINE RAFFAELE
PHOTO: ERIC VON LOCKHART

FORMALS

PIERRE AND CARLO
HAIR: ANGELA FONG
MAKE-UP: HARRIET GOLDMAN
PHOTO: MILTON PERRY

PIERRE AND CARLO
HAIR: MICHAEL MCVEY
MAKE-UP: HARRIET GOLDMAN
PHOTO: MILTON PERRY

PIERRE AND CARLO
HAIR: CHRISTINE D"ALONZO
MAKE-UP: HARRIET GOLDMAN
PHOTO: MILTON PERRY

PIERRE AND CARLO
HAIR & MAKE-UP: LAURENTIUS PURNAMA
PHOTO: MILTON PERRY

PIERRE AND CARLO
HAIR & MAKE-UP: LAURENTIUS PURNAMA
PHOTO: MILTON PERRY

57

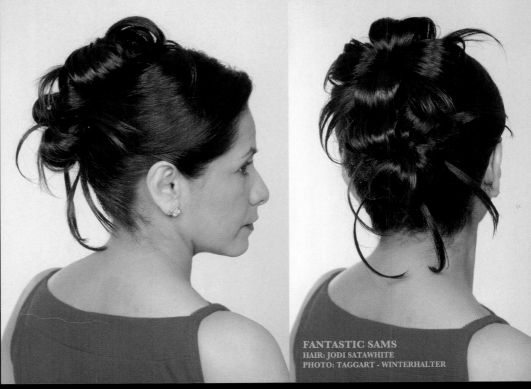

FANTASTIC SAMS
HAIR: JODI SATAWHITE
PHOTO: TAGGART - WINTERHALTER

DIZIN SALON
HAIR: BETH ECKEL
PHOTO: BETH ECKEL

ANTASTIC SAMS
IR: PRINCY SEBASTIAN
OTO: TAGGART - WINTERHALTER

FORMALS

59

FANTASTIC SAMS
HAIR: KARNE CHARO
PHOTO: TAGGART - WINTERHALTER

FANTASTIC SAMS
HAIR: MARIA E. VELASCO
PHOTO: TAGGART - WINTERHALTER

FANTASTIC SAMS
HAIR: ANNA MARIA TAYLOR
PHOTO: TAGGART - WINTERHALTER

FANTASTIC SAMS
HAIR: SHAREN OWENS
PHOTO: TAGGART - WINTERHALTER

FANTASTIC SAMS
HAIR: SHAREN OWENS
PHOTO: TAGGART - WINTERHALTER

FANTASTIC SAMS
HAIR: PATRICIA QUIROZ
PHOTO: TAGGART - WINTERHALTER

FANTASTIC SAMS
HAIR: ALEXANDRIA NEWLIN
PHOTO: TAGGART - WINTERHALTER

ARTISTIC HAIR
HAIR: NICOLE HARDIN
MAKE-UP: ROSE MARIE
PHOTO: TAGGART - WINTERHALTER

FANTASTIC SAMS
HAIR: NANCY SIMMONS
PHOTO: TAGGART - WINTERHALTER

FORMALS

ARTISTIC HAIR
HAIR: COLLEEN CLARKE
PHOTO: TAGGART - WINTERHALTER

ARTISTIC HAIR
HAIR: JILL KESTER / MARILYN PINNIX
PHOTO: TAGGART - WINTERHALTER

ARTISTIC HAIR
HAIR: MARILYN PINNIX
PHOTO: TAGGART - WINTERHALTER

ARTISTIC HAIR
HAIR: JILL KESTER
PHOTO: TAGGART - WINTERHALTER

FANTASTIC SAMS
HAIR: ANNA MARIA TAYLOR
PHOTO: TAGGART - WINTERHALTER

FANTASTIC SAMS
HAIR: YONG KIM
PHOTO: TAGGART - WINTERHALTER

FANTASTIC SAMS
HAIR: DEYANIRA MORENO
PHOTO: TAGGART - WINTERHALTER

FANTASTIC SAMS
HAIR: MINA ASHRAFNIA
PHOTO: TAGGART - WINTERHALTER

BAZZAK HAIR DESIGN & DAY SPA
HAIR: ANNETTE LANE
MAKE-UP: ANNETTE LANE
PHOTO: TOM CARSON

GEORGE FOUR SEASONS
SPA SALON
HAIR: CHRISTELLE ERROT
MAKE-UP: BETH FARMER
PHOTO: TOM CARSON

FANTASTIC SAMS
HAIR: BARBARA LEAL
PHOTO: TAGGART - WINTERHALTER

ANTASTIC SAMS
AIR: RASHIDAH THOMAS EADY
OTO: TAGGART - WINTERHALTER

FANTASTIC SAMS
HAIR: SASKIA OSBORN-SEVEY
PHOTO: TAGGART - WINTERHALTER

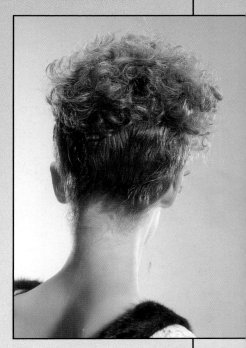

FANTASTIC SAMS
HAIR: JESUS MANCILLA
PHOTO: TAGGART - WINTERHALTER

FORMALS

FANTASTIC SAMS
HAIR: ESTHER MORALES
PHOTO: TAGGART - WINTERHALTER

72

FANTASTIC SAMS
HAIR: BARBARA ANN SILVAS
PHOTO: TAGGART - WINTERHALTER

FANTASTIC SAMS
HAIR: ESTHER MORALES
PHOTO: TAGGART - WINTERHALTER

ARTISTIC HAIR
HAIR: NICOLE HARDEN
PHOTO: TAGGART - WINTERHALTER

FANTASTIC SAMS
HAIR: SOCO BECERRA
PHOTO: TAGGART - WINTERHALTER

FANTASTIC SAMS
HAIR: BARBARA LEAL
PHOTO: TAGGART - WINTERHALTER

INTERCOIFFURE
HAIR: DAVID PORRIS / JOHN DONATO
MAKE-UP: BARBARA ALEXANDER
PHOTO: KINT QUON

COIFFINA COIFFURE

INTERCOIFFURE
HAIR: DAVID PORRIS
MAKE-UP: BARBARA ALEXANDER
PHOTO: KINT QUON

COIFFINA COIFFURE

FORMALS

HAIRBOUTIQUE.COM
HAIR: BARBARA LHOTAN
MAKE-UP: CATHERINE RAFFAELA
PHOTO: ERIC VON LOCKHART

HAIRBOUTIQUE.COM
HAIR: BARBARA LHOTAN
MAKE-UP: CATHERINE RAFFAELA
PHOTO: ERIC VON LOCKHART

HAIRBOUTIQUE.COM
HAIR: BARBARA LHOTAN
MAKE-UP: CATHERINE RAFFAELA
PHOTO: ERIC VON LOCKHART

ROBERT OF PHILADELPHIA
HAIR: LOUIS SALVATI
MAKE-UP: ANDREY
PHOTO: ERIC VON LOCKHART

HAIRBOUTIQUE.COM
HAIR: BARBARA LHOTAN
MAKE-UP: CATHERINE RAFFAELA
PHOTO: ERIC VON LOCKHART

FORMALS

A true inspiration, this creation features a statement of texture (and color too, with a daring red hairpiece) while allowing the long hair goddess short hair sass!

PIVOT POINT
HAIR: PATRICK KALLE
MAKE-UP: LORI NEAPOLITAN
PHOTO: DAVID PLACEK

PIVOT POINT
HAIR: VASILIKI STAVRAKIS
MAKE-UP: LORI NEAPOLITAN
PHOTO: DAVID PLACEK

Strong and innovative, a way to combine techniques that harmonize with each other. She is a masterpiece in design.

Artistically curvaceous, this look is what she is meant to wear! Looping visual patterns - created by dressing the hair in just the right direction are enhanced with hairpieces of contrasting color.

PIVOT POINT
HAIR: VASILIKI STAVRAKIS
MAKE-UP: LORI NEAPOLITAN
PHOTO: DAVID PLACEK

PIVOT POINT
HAIR: SABINE HELD-PEREZ
MAKE-UP: LORI NEAPOLITAN
PHOTO: DAVID PLACEK

A dramatic change in texture makes a signature statement in this long hair design. Soft and romantic, and not overly curly, the shape is extraordinary and completely unique.

PIVOT POINT
HAIR: SABINE HELD-PEREZ
MAKE-UP: LORI NEAPOLITAN
PHOTO: DAVID PLACEK

The avant-garde goddess is a timeless beauty. Her statement is a look of classic simplicity with ornamental braids (and hairpieces too) that loop and fold to complete the design.

PIVOT POINT
HAIR:SABINE HELD-PEREZ
MAKE-UP: LORI NEAPOLITAN
PHOTO: DAVID PLACEK

Smooth and sexy, a clean look is an expressive design for the perfect formal affair.

PIVOT POINT
HAIR: DANNY VALLES
MAKE-UP: LORI NEAPOLITAN
PHOTO: DAVID PLACEK

Spontaneously sophisticated, she captures the freshness of youth while defining formal elegance.

By incorporating a tantalizing mix of twisting, folding and looping, this composition creates an exotic and finely sculpted look.

Brides

FANTASTIC SAMS
HAIR: JOLENE TORRES
MAKE-UP: JAMIE QUEENIN
PHOTO: TAGGART - WINTERHALTER

FANTASTIC SAMS
HAIR: MARY MELTON
PHOTO: TAGGART - WINTERHALTER

*Many younger brides
are opting for a down style.*

*Nicole Simmons Meyers
Garbos Salon*

Bridal hair. …It's all about elegance.

*Jennifer Metzger
Fantastic Sams*

A simple style can be incredibly elegant.

*Nicole Simmons Meyers
Garbos Salon*

GARBOS SALON
HAIR: NICOLE SIMMONS MEYERS
MAKE-UP: JAMIE QEENIN
PHOTO: TAGGART - WINTERHALTER

FANTASTIC SAMS
HAIR: JENNIFER METZGER
PHOTO: TAGGART - WINTERHALTER

Curls make for a beautiful textured bridal style.

Laura Croft
Vibe Studio

VIBE STUDIO
HAIR: LAURA CROFT
MAKE-UP: JAMIE QEENIN
PHOTO: TAGGART - WINTERHALTER

FANTASTIC SAMS
HAIR: MARIA QUIROZ
PHOTO: TAGGART - WINTERHALTER

For this elegant bride, I swept the hair upward and overlapped sections in back to create a finished zigzag effect. The balance was pinned up at the crown and rolled back onto itself – a tiara completes the style.

Maria Quiroz - Fantastic Sams

A series
of knots
were created
that were almost
chain - linked
together.

Laura Croft
Vibe Studio

VIBE STUDIO
HAIR: LAURA CROFT
MAKE-UP: JAMIE QEENIN
PHOTO: TAGGART - WINTERHALTER

BRIDES

I like to allow for a little depth
in a formal style with darker roots.

Jennifer Hays, Pon International

PON INTERNATIONAL
HAIR: JENNIFER HAYS
MAKE-UP: JAMIE QEENIN
PHOTO: TAGGART - WINTERHALTER

SALON BOUCLE
HAIR: AZI SEDEHI
MAKE-UP: JAMIE QEENIN
PHOTO: TAGGART - WINTERHALTER

FANTASTIC SAMS
HAIR: BRITTANY JUSTICE
MAKE-UP: JAMIE QEENIN
PHOTO: TAGGART - WINTERHALTER

I believe that formal styles
need to be highly personalized
for brides on their special day.

Brittany Justice - Fantastic Sams

Make a stunning entrance
with this elegant up style.

Azi Sedehi - Salon Boucle

MLD III SALON STUDIO
HAIR: SANDRA CHANDLER
MAKE-UP: LISA WEST
PHOTO: BILL BAKER

MLD III SALON STUDIO
HAIR: SANDRA CHANDLER
MAKE-UP: LISA WEST
PHOTO: BILL BAKER

VICTOR BALESTRI SALON
HAIR: FRANK J. DIBRINO
PHOTO: DAVID GUARINO

MLD III SALON STUDIO
HAIR: SANDRA CHANDLER
MAKE-UP: CAROLINA SAA
PHOTO: BILL BAKER

GARBOS SALON
HAIR: NICOLE SIMMONS MEYERS
MAKE-UP: JAMIE QEENIN
PHOTO: TAGGART - WINTERHALTER

Get Your Work Published!

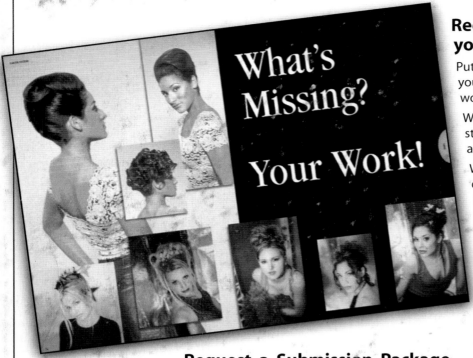

Receive International Recognition when you publish your work in Inspire

Put your name in the limelight and receive the recognition your hard work deserves. Inspire is the only place to be for worldwide recognition.

We are always looking for the latest fresh new looks and styles that are fashionable as well as commercial and are appropriate for salon clientele.

We are looking for handsome men and gorgeous women of all ages to portray the latest new looks and trends. No fantasy work please!

It's So Easy!

Professional photography and good looking models are key to having your work published. Please send only very clean, well protected color slides and transparencies or black and white glossies. Remember to label all your slides with proper credits and submit them with an Inspire model release form.

Request a Submission Package

All the forms and information you need to submit high quality work in one package. AND, if your work is chosen to be in Inspire you'll receive a complimentary book and press release package as our way of saying thanks. Your hard work deserves recognition from your community as well as internationally. Send the press release to the local newspapers, radio stations…Even TV! The response will surprise you.

Call **(800) 634-8500**   Email: **inspire@connix.com**
or visit our website at **www.inspirequarterly.com** to download the forms.

SUBMISSION DEADLINES
- **March 15**   • **June 15**   • **September 15**   • **December 15**

Looking for a GREAT hair photographer?   Try one of ours.

Purely Visual Productions
8502 E. Chapman Ave., Suite #610
Orange Hills CA 92869
(714) 532-4772 Phone
(714) 532-4660 Fax
ibvisual@aol.com

Eric Von Lockhart Photography
48 West 21st Street
New York NY 10010
(212) 463-0450
evlone@earthlink.net

Tom Carson Photography
611 Ashworth Rd.
Charlotte NC 28211
(704) 364-6457

Que manque-t-il à cette photo?
Votre Travail!
Faites publier vos photos!

Tout le monde souhaite voir ses talents et ses qualités reconnus. Quelle place pourrait être meilleure qu' INSPIRE pour vous faire connaitre?

Nous sommes intéressés de recevoir des photos de coiffures mode destinées aux clientes des salons de coiffure. Nous sommes avides de beaux modèles, de tous âges, hommes ou femmes, mais pas de travaux de haute fantaisie.

De façon à vous faire connaître, indiquez sur chaque photo: le nom du salon, le nom du coiffeur, du maquilleur, et du photographe.

S'il vous plaît n'envoyez que des dias ou négatifs couleurs de bonne qualité ou des photos noir et blanc. Joignez à chaque photo les informations précisées ci-dessus.

Vous êtes intéressé! Bravo!

Pour plus d'information sur la facon de nous transmettre vos photos, téléphonez ou écrivez à notre distributeur officiel.

Que es lo que falta en este retrato?
Tu Trabajo!
Consiga Su Trabajo Publicado!

Todo mundo tiene el deseo de que su talento y habilidades sean reconocidas.

Que mejor lugar que Inspire para recibir este reconocimiento estamos muy interesados en recibir fotografias de modas y aspectos apropiados, para la clientela de salon de belleza.

Nosotros estamos buscando modelos tanto de hombre como de mujer en cualquier edad. No queremos fotos con peinados de fantasta.

Para recibir lo anterior y darle su credito, favor de enviar fotografias muy claras, una por modelo. Favor de enviar fotografias y/o transparencias, muy bien protegidas enviando carta, dando su permiso para la publicacion de la foto.

Esta ud interesado! Grandioso!

Para major informacion de como enviar fotos. Formas de permiso de publicacion para posibles se iones de fotos tomadas en su area. Llamenos o escribanos para recibir guia completa.